The Easy

Instrumental Classics
23 classic songs for keyboard

Published 1994

Music arranged & processed by Barnes Music Engraving Ltd East Sussex TN34 1HA
Cover Images The Music Vault (with thanks to Vicky Carrick)

© International Music Publications Ltd
Griffin House 161 Hammersmith Road London England W6 8BS

APACHE

By Jerry Lordan

Suggested Registration: Pan Pipes
Rhythm: Beguine / Latin
Tempo: ♩ = 132

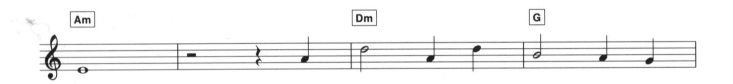

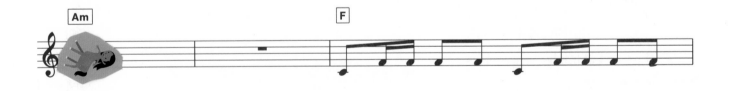

3

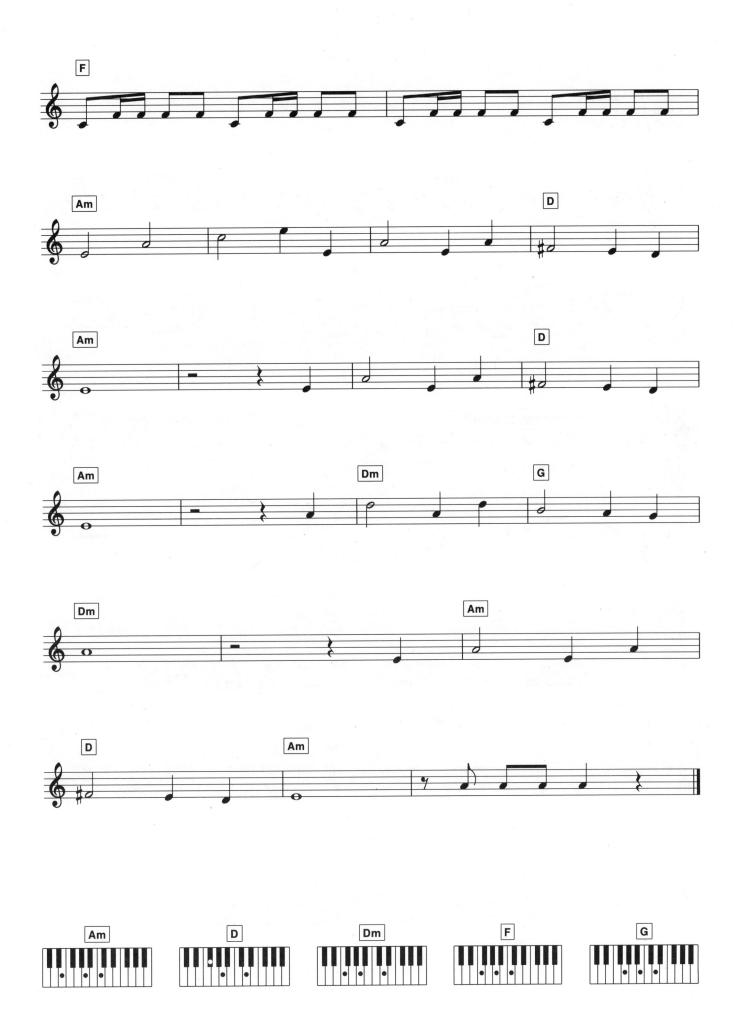

4

Axel F

By Harold Faltermeyer

Suggested Registration: Synth Lead
Rhythm: Elec. Pop
Tempo: ♩ = 112

5

Cavatina

By Stanley Myers

Suggested Registration: Strings
Rhythm: Pop Waltz
Tempo: ♩ = 100

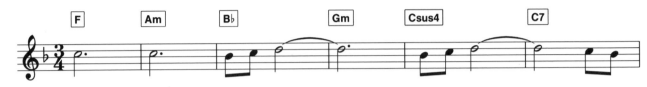

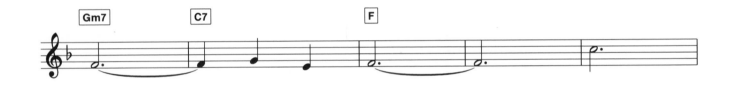

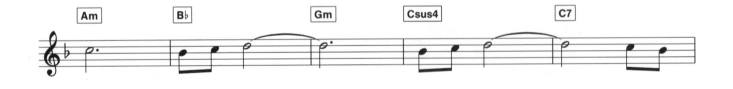

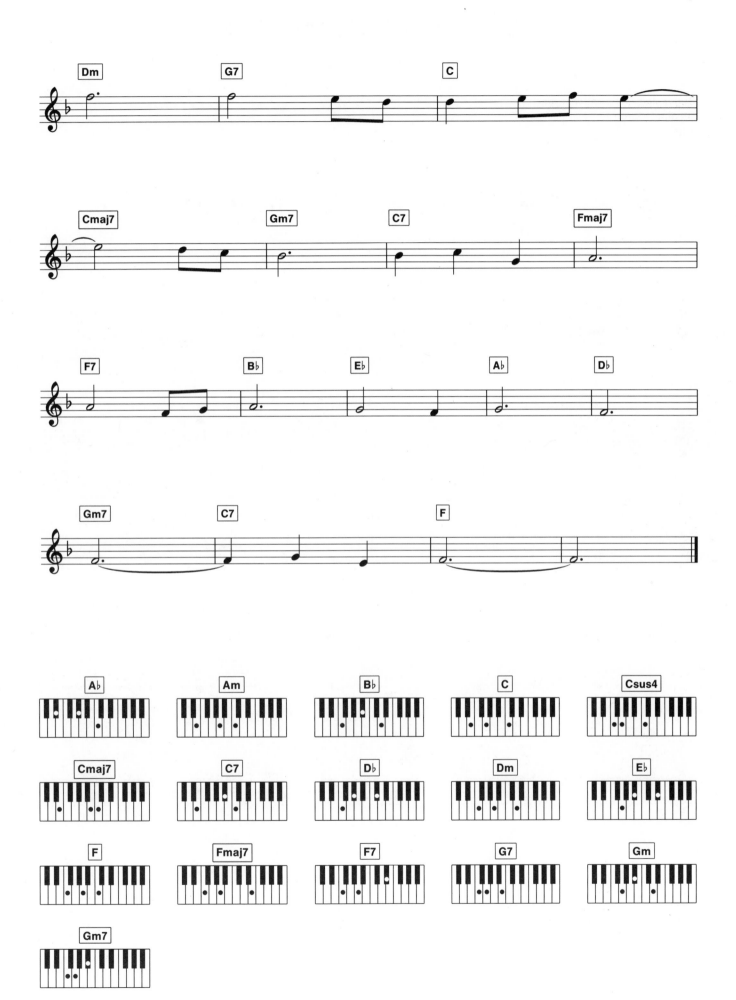

Dambuster's March

By Eric Coates

Suggested Registration: French Horn
Rhythm: March
Tempo: ♩ = 92

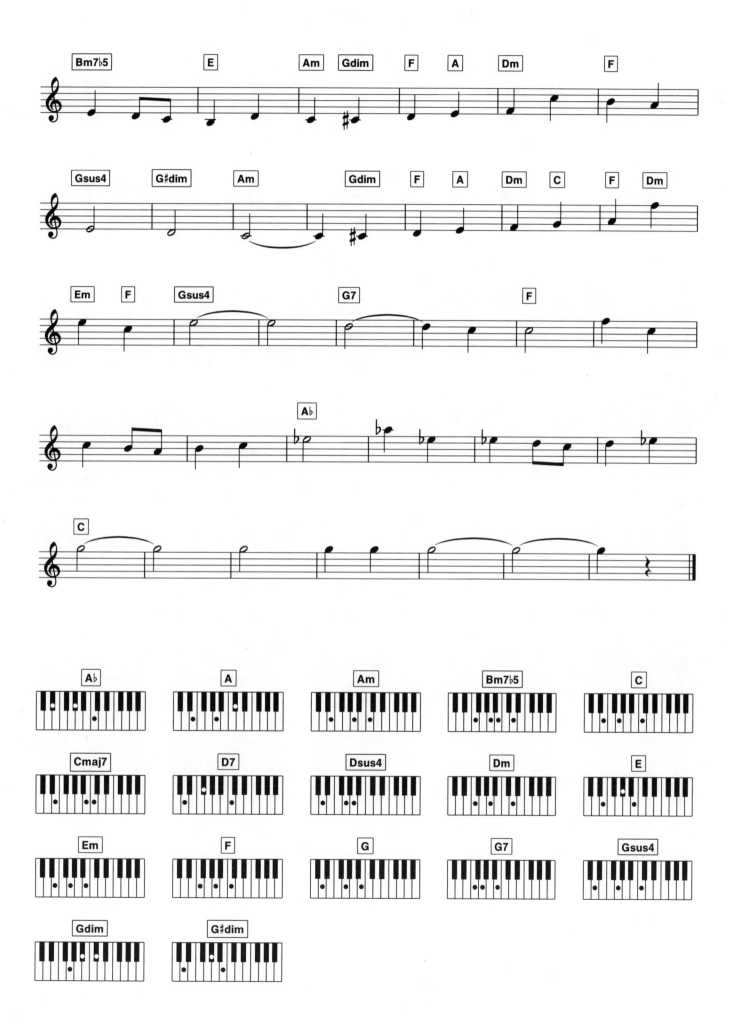

The Entertainer

By Scott Joplin

Suggested Registration: Honkytonk Piano
Rhythm: Ragtime / Dixieland
Tempo: ♩ = 112

THE FLORAL DANCE

By Katie Moss

Suggested Registration: Accordian
Rhythm: March
Tempo: ♩ = 160

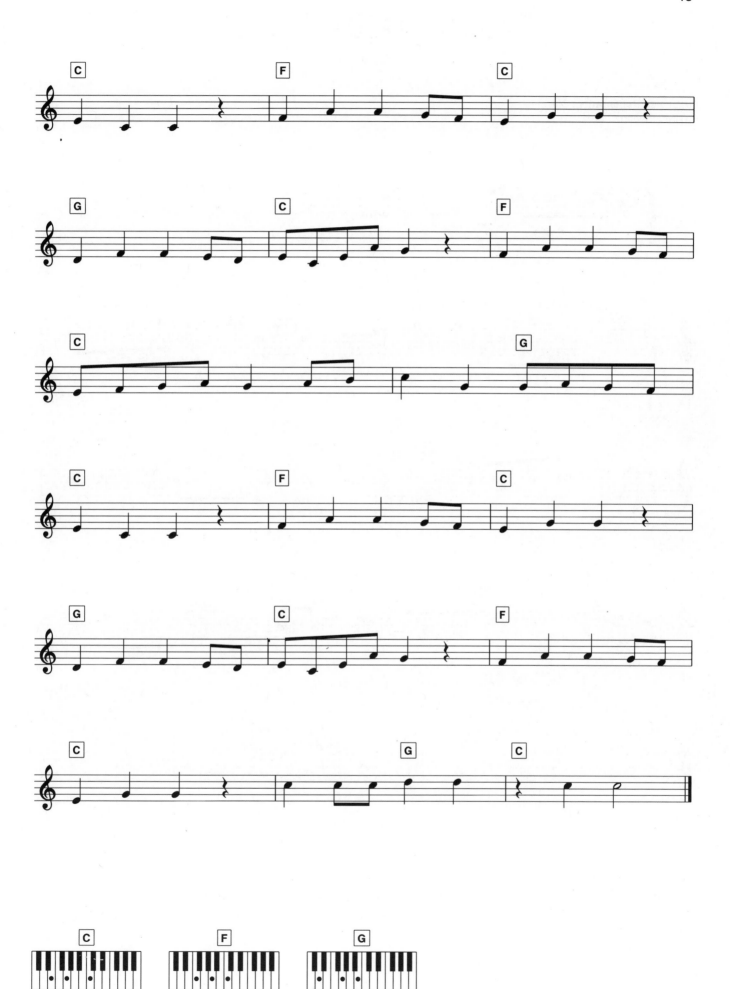

THE HOUSE OF ELIOTT

By Jim Parker

Suggested Registration: Clarinet
Rhythm: Swing / Jazz   *RAGTIME !?   SWING*
Tempo: ♩ = 104

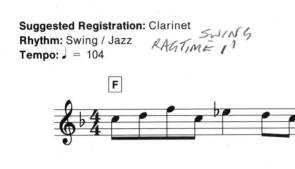

THE HUSTLE

By Van McCoy

Suggested Registration: Flute
Rhythm: 16 Beat
Tempo: ♩ = 98

THE JAMES BOND THEME

By Monty Norman

Suggested Registration: Electric Guitar
Rhythm: 8 Beat
Tempo: ♩ = 118

19

Lara's Theme
From "Doctor Zhivago"

By Maurice Jarre

Suggested Registration: Strings
Rhythm: Waltz
Tempo: ♩ = 154

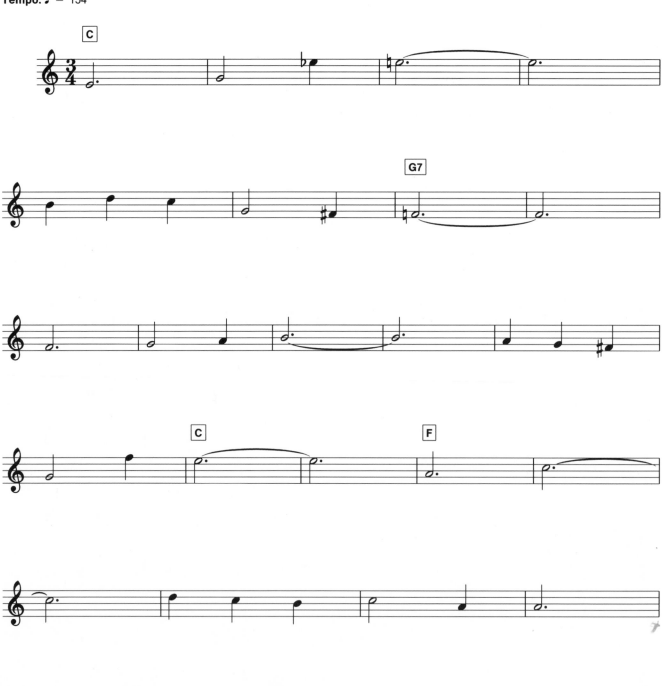

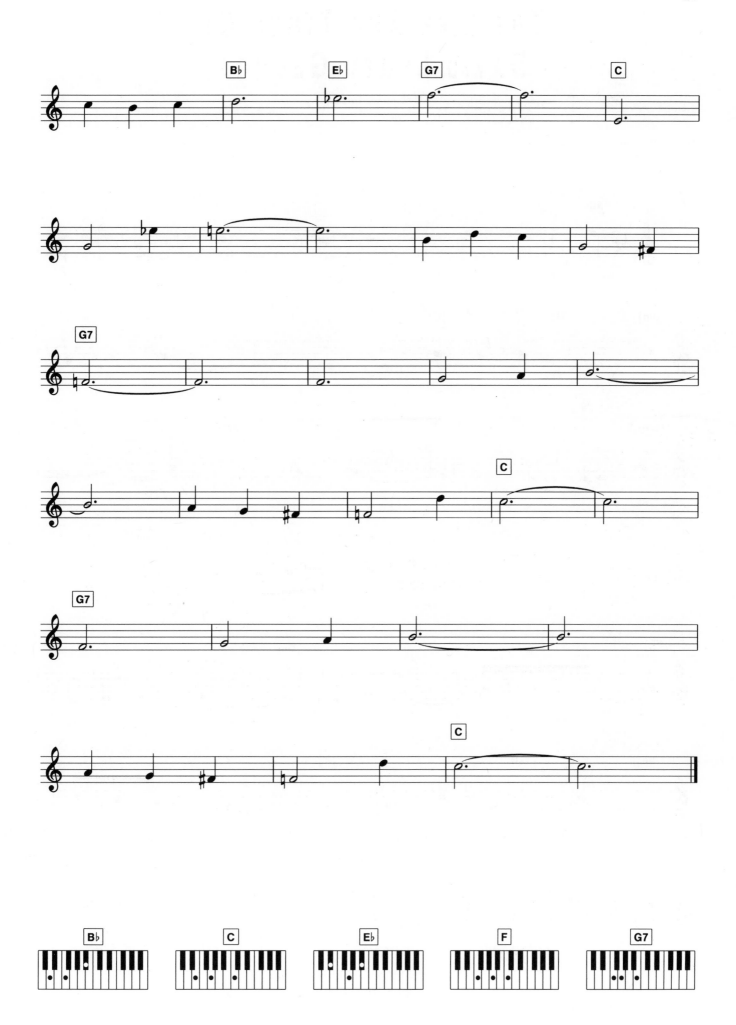

The Life And Times Of David Lloyd George

By Ennio Morricone

Suggested Registration: Strings
Rhythm: Slow Rock 6/8
Tempo: ♩. = 60 (♪ = 180)

March Of The Mods
(The Finnjenka Dance)

By Tony Carr

Suggested Registration: Trumpet
Rhythm: 6/8 March
Tempo: ♩ = 104

MEXICAN HAT DANCE

Traditional

Suggested Registration: Pan Pipes
Rhythm: 6/8 March
Tempo: ♩. = 98

THE PINK PANTHER

By Henry Mancini

Suggested Registration: Tenor Saxophone
Rhythm: Swing
Tempo: ♩ = 98

POPCORN

By Gershon Kingsley

Suggested Registration: Pop Lead
Rhythm: Elec. Pop
Tempo: ♩ = 112

Star Wars (Main Title)

By John Williams

Suggested Registration: Trumpet
Rhythm: March 6/8
Tempo: ♩ = 112

STRANGER ON THE SHORE

Words by Robert Mellin / Music by Acker Bilk

Suggested Registration: Clarinet
Rhythm: Soft Rock
Tempo: ♩ = 92

The Stripper

By David D Rose

Suggested Registration: Trombone
Rhythm: Jazz / Swing
Tempo: ♩ = 90

Telstar

By Joe Meek

Suggested Registration: Strings
Rhythm: Beguine / Latin
Tempo: ♩ = 132

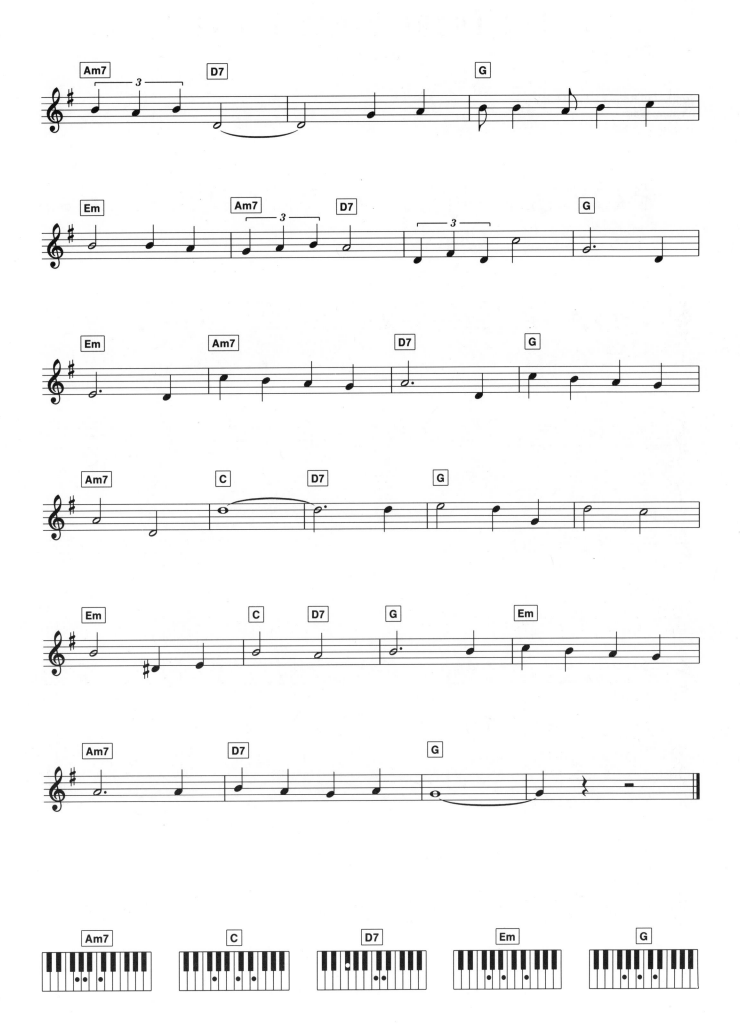

THE THORN BIRDS THEME

By Henry Mancini

Suggested Registration: Flute
Rhythm: Waltz
Tempo: ♩ = 132

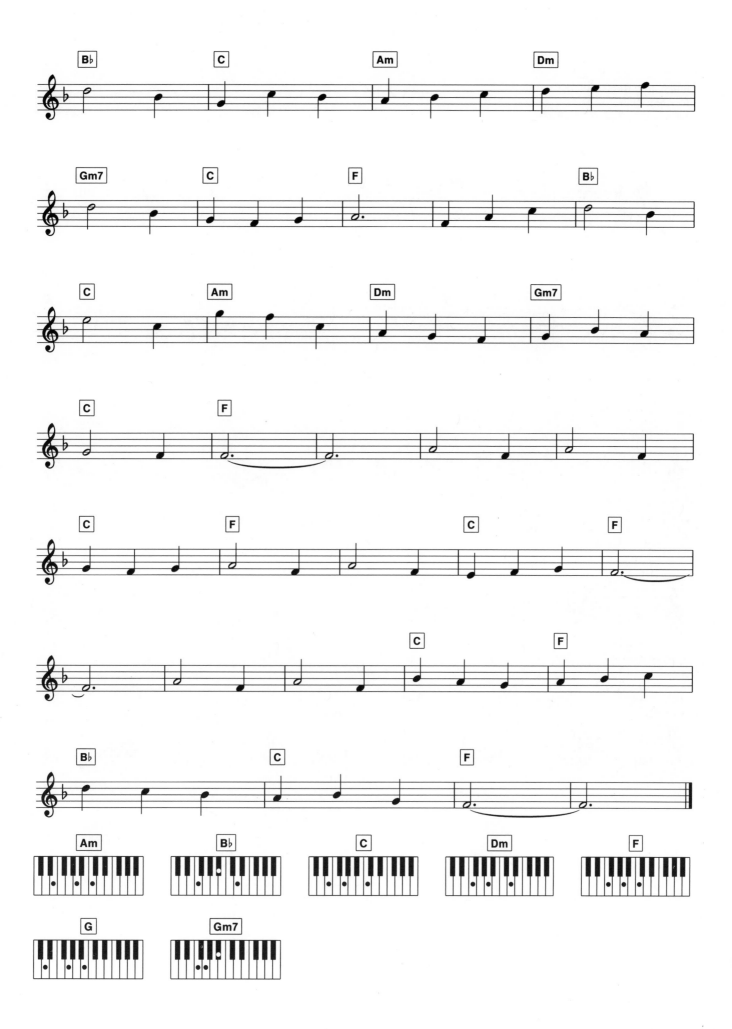

THREE QUARTER BLUES

By George Gershwin and Ira Gershwin

Suggested Registration: Clarinet
Rhythm: Waltz
Tempo: ♩ = 142

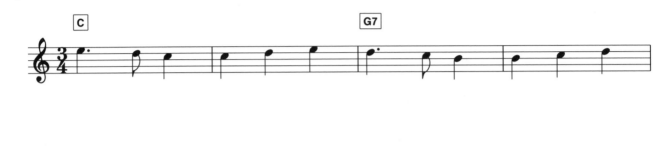

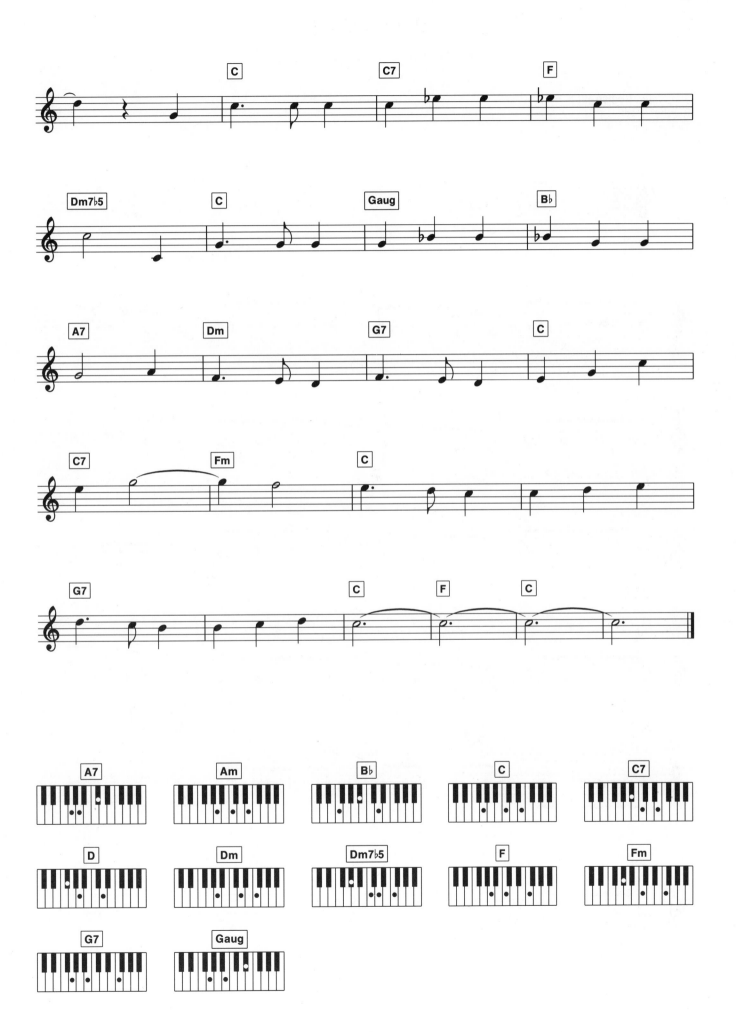

Wipeout

By Wilson, Fuller, Berryhill and Connolly

Suggested Registration: Electric Guitar
Rhythm: Rock
Tempo: ♩ = 132

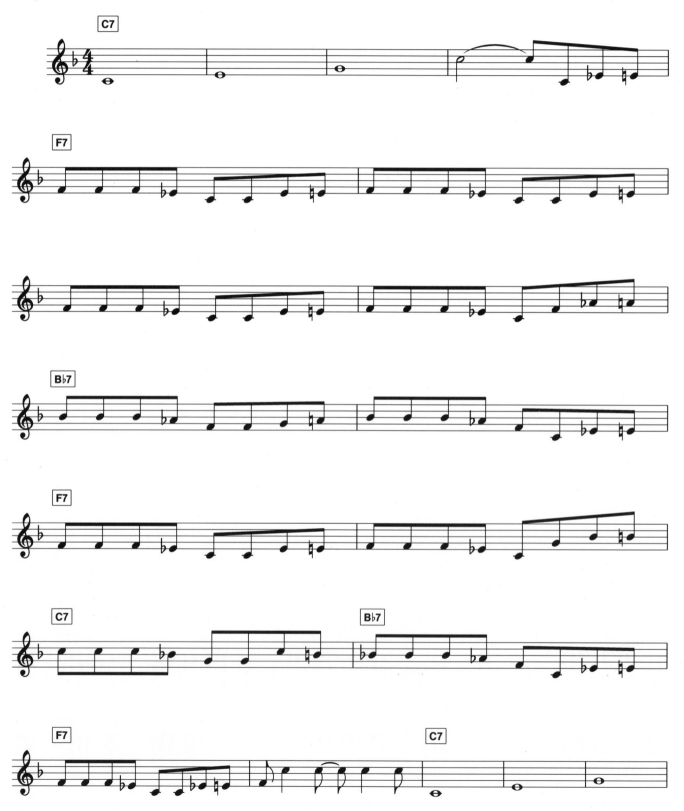

633 SQUADRON

By Ron Goodwin

Suggested Registration: French Horn
Rhythm: 6/8 March
Tempo: ♩. = 104

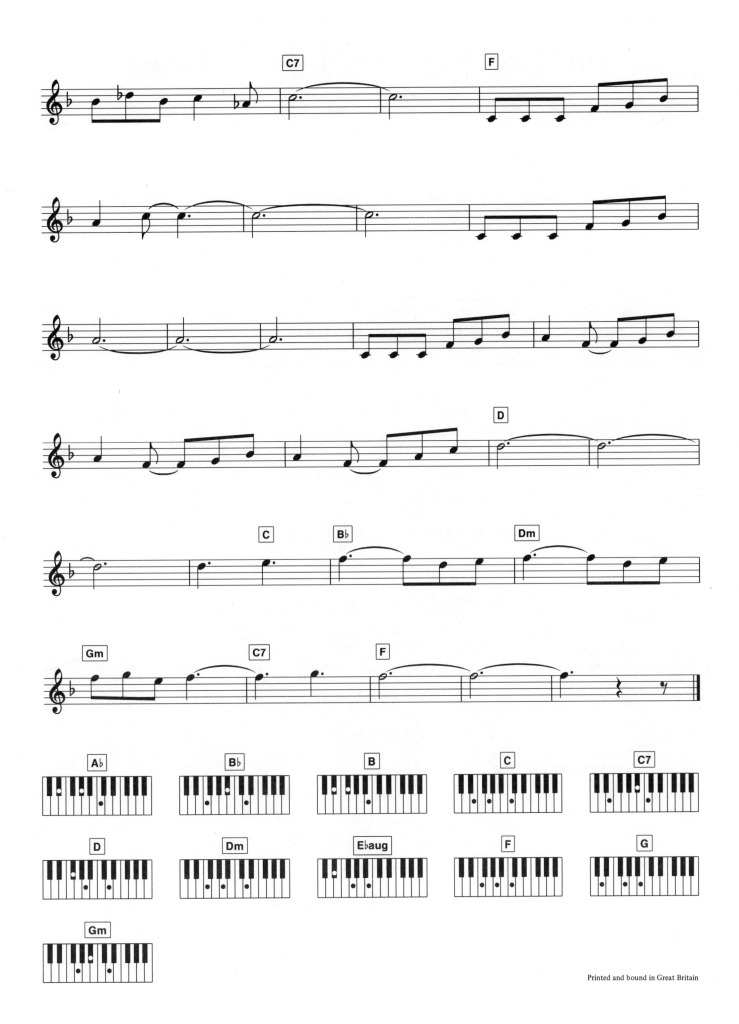

Printed and bound in Great Britain

The Easy Keyboard Library Series

Big Band Hits
Order Ref: 19098

Popular Classics
Order Ref: 4180A

Blues
Order Ref: 3477A

Pub Singalong Collection
Order Ref: 3954A

Celebration Songs
Order Ref: 3478A

Rock 'n' Roll Classics
Order Ref: 2224A

Christmas Carols
Order Ref: 4616A

Traditional Scottish Favourites
Order Ref: 4231A

Christmas Songs
Order Ref: 19198

Showtunes - Volume 1
Order Ref: 19103

Classic Hits - Volume 1
Order Ref: 19099

Showtunes - Volume 2
Order Ref: 3328A

Classic Hits - Volume 2
Order Ref: 19100

Soft Rock Collection
Order Ref: 4617A

Country Songs
Order Ref: 19101

Soul Classics
Order Ref: 19201

Traditional English Favourites
Order Ref: 4229A

Summer Collection
Order Ref: 3489A

Favourite Hymns
Order Ref: 4179A

TV Themes
Order Ref: 19196

Film Classics
Order Ref: 19197

The Twenties
Order Ref: 2969A

Great Songwriters
Order Ref: 2225A

The Thirties
Order Ref: 2970A

Instrumental Classics
Order Ref: 2338A

The Forties
Order Ref: 2971A

Traditional Irish Favourites
Order Ref: 4230A

The Fifties
Order Ref: 2972A

Love Songs - Volume 1
Order Ref: 19102

The Sixties
Order Ref: 2973A

Love Songs - Volume 2
Order Ref: 19199

The Seventies
Order Ref: 2974A

Music Hall
Order Ref: 3329A

The Eighties
Order Ref: 2975A

Motown Classics
Order Ref: 2337A

The Nineties
Order Ref: 2976A

Number One Hits
Order Ref: 19200

Wartime Collection
Order Ref: 3955A

Wedding Collection
Order Ref: 3688A

Exclusive distributors:

International Music Publications Limited
Griffin House 161 Hammersmith Road London W6 8BS, England
International Music Publications Limited
25 Rue D'Hauteville, 75010 Paris, France
International Music Publications GmbH Germany
Marstallstrasse 8, D-80539 München, Germany
Nuova Carisch S.R.L.
Via M.F. Quintiliano 40, 20138 Milano, Italy
Danmusik
Vognmagergade 7, DK-1120 Copenhagen K, Denmark

THE EASY KEYBOARD LIBRARY